It's Easy To Play Pops.

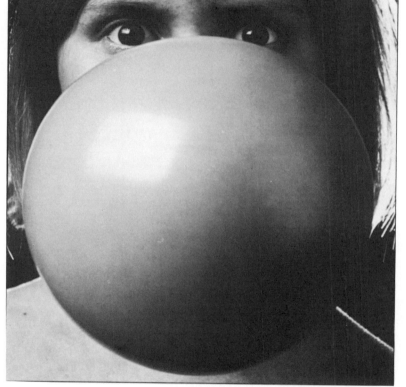

Wise Publications
London/New York/Sydney/Cologne

Exclusive Distributors:
Music Sales Limited
8/9 Frith Street, London, W1V 5TZ, England.
Music Sales Pty. Limited
120 Rothschild Avenue, Rosebery, NSW 2018, Australia.

This book © Copyright 1981 by
Wise Publications
ISBN 0.86001.782.6
Order No. AM 27228

Cover by Pearce Marchbank
Cover Photograph by Gered Mankowitz
Compilation by Peter Evans
Arranged by Cyril Watters

Music Sales complete catalogue lists thousands
of titles and is free from your local music
book shop, or direct from Music Sales Limited.
Please send £1 in stamps for postage to
Music Sales Limited, 8/9 Frith Street, London W1V 5TZ.

**Printed in England by
Eyre & Spottiswoode Limited,
London and Margate, Kent**

I Will Survive

Words and Music by Dino Fekaris and Freddie Perren

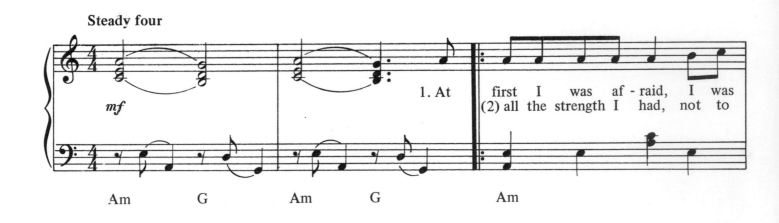

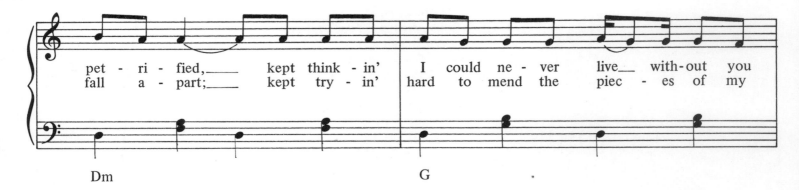

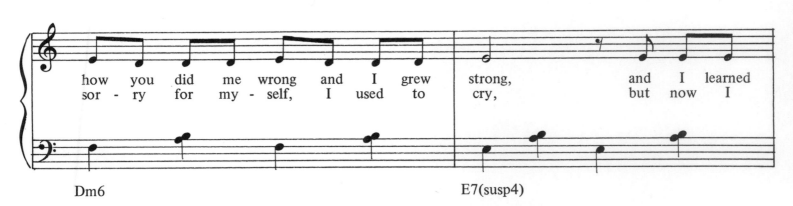

how to get a-long, and so you're back
hold my head up high. And you see

E7

me,
from out-er

Am
some-bod-y
space.

Dm
new,

I just walk
I'm not that

in to find you here with that sad
chained up lit-tle per-son still in

G

look up-on your face. I should have
love with you. _____ And so you

C

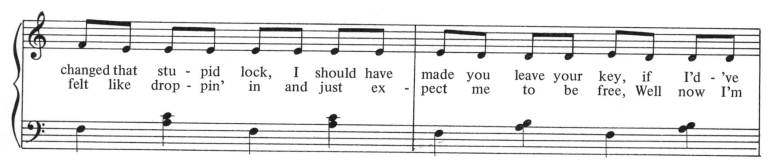

changed that stu-pid lock, I should have
felt like drop-pin' in and just ex-

Fmaj7

made you leave your key, if I'd-'ve
pect me to be free, Well now I'm

Dm6

known for just one se-cond you'd be
sav-in' all my lov-in' for some-

E7(susp4)

back to bo-ther me.
one who's lov-in' me.

E7
{Go on now go,

Am
walk out the

door; just turn a-

Dm

round, now, 'cause you're not

G

wel-come an-y more.

C

Weren't you the one who tried to hurt me with good-bye? Did you think I'd

Fmaj7   Dm6

-

crum - ble,   did you think I'd lay down__ and die? Oh no, not

E7(susp4)   E7

I.   I will sur - vive.__ Oh, as long as I know how to love, I

Am   Dm   G

know I'll stay a - live. I've got all my life to live, I've got

C   Fmaj7

D.%. 2nd time and Fade

all my love to give and I'll sur - vive,   I will sur - vive. 2. It took
                                                                 Now

Dm6   E7(susp4)   E7

Thank You For The Music

Words and Music by Benny Andersson and Bjorn Ulvaeus

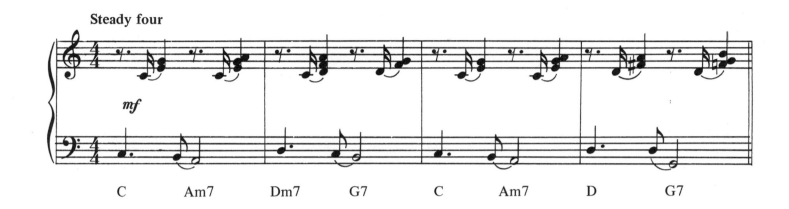

C   Am7   Dm7   G7   C   Am7   D   G7

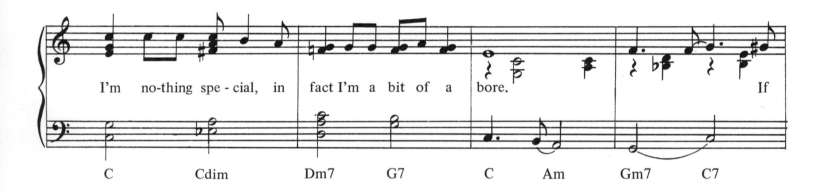

I'm no-thing spe - cial, in fact I'm a bit of a bore.

C   Cdim   Dm7   G7   C   Am   Gm7   C7   If

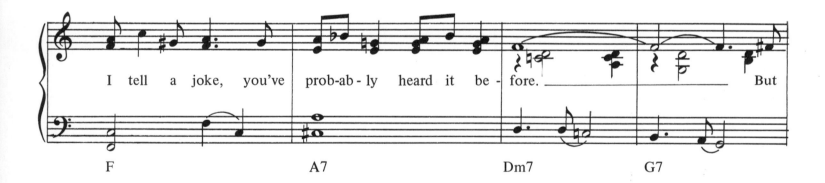

I tell a joke, you've prob-ab - ly heard it be - fore. _____ But

F   A7   Dm7   G7

I have a tal - ent, a won-der-ful thing, 'Cause ev - 'ry-one lis - tens when

C   G   Am7

I start to sing, I'm so grate-ful and proud. _____ All I

F   Fm   Am   C+   C6

want is to sing__ it out loud. So I say thank you for the mu-sic, the

F   G7 Am7 G   C   Dm

songs I'm sing-ing. Thanks for all the joy they're bring-ing. Who can live with-out it? I

F G7 C   Am   C   D7   G7   C   Dm

ask in all hon - es - ty, what would life be with-out a

E7   Am   Fmaj7 F6   Fm

song or dance,__what are we? So I say, thank you for the mu-sic, for

C   C7 Gm7 A7   F

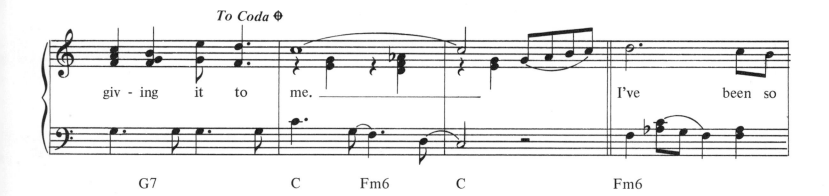

To Coda ⊕

giv - ing it to me._____ I've been so

G7　　　　C　Fm6　　C　　　　Fm6

luck-y___ I am the girl with gol - den hair. I wan-na sing it out to

C　　　　Fm　Fm6　　C　　　　Fm　E7

D.℞. al Coda

ev - 'ry - bo - dy, what a joy, what a life, what a chance._____

Am　　　　Dm7　　　　　　G7

⊕ *CODA*

me.　　　　　　　　So I say thank you for the mu-sic, for

C　　C7　　A7　　Dm A7　F

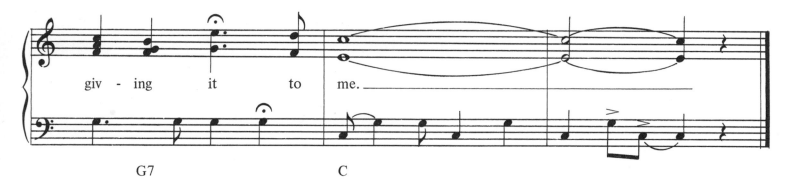

giv - ing it to me._____

G7　　　　　C

Song For Guy

By Elton John

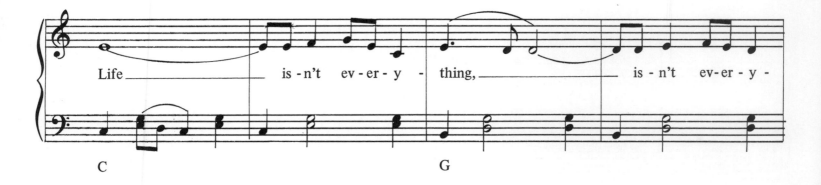

thing, _____ is - n't ev - er - y - thing. _____

Bb   F

C   F6   C   C   F6   C

D.%. al Coda

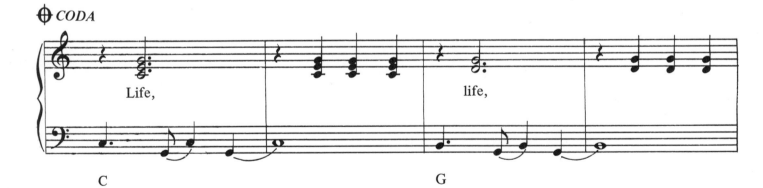

F   G7   F   C

⊕ *CODA*

Life,   life,

C   G

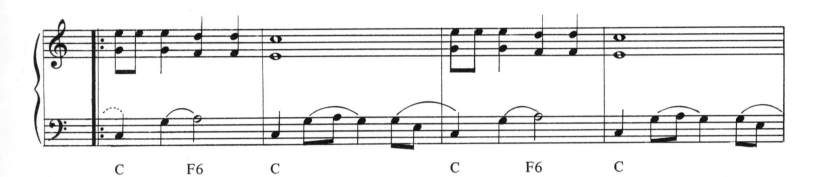

life,   life,   life. _____ *pp*

Bb   F

11

Something

Words and Music by George Harrison

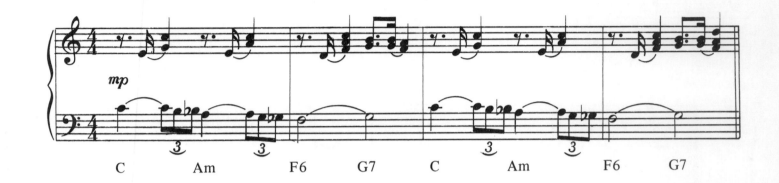

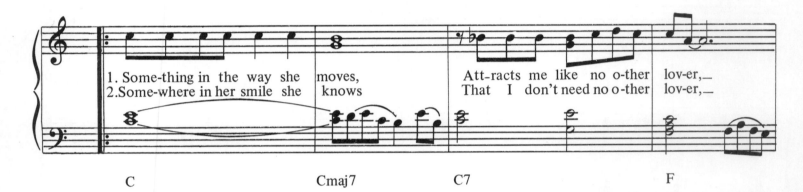

1. Some-thing in the way she moves,
2. Some-where in her smile she knows

Att-racts me like no o-ther lov-er,__
That I don't need no o-ther lov-er,__

Some-thing in the way she woos me.__
Some-thing in her style that shows me.__

I don't want to leave_ her now, you

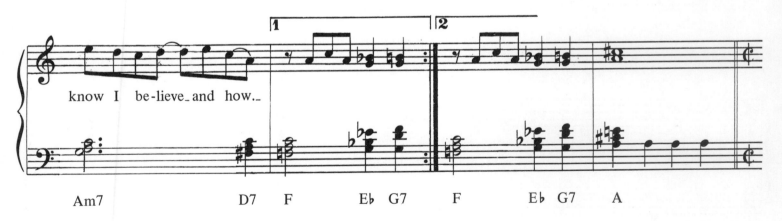

know I be-lieve_ and how..

(A)   Amaj7   F♯m   A

1. You're ask - ing me, will my_ love grow?_____ I don't
2. You stick a - round, now it _ may show._____

D   G   A7

know; _____ I don't know. _____

C   (C)   Cmaj7

know. _____ Some-thing in the way she knows

C7   F   D7   G

and all I have to do is think of her. some-thing in the way she shows me._ I

Am   Am7   D7   F   E♭   G7   C

don't want to leave her now, you. know I be - lieve_and how_ *ritard.*

13

Just The Way You Are

Words and Music by Billy Joel

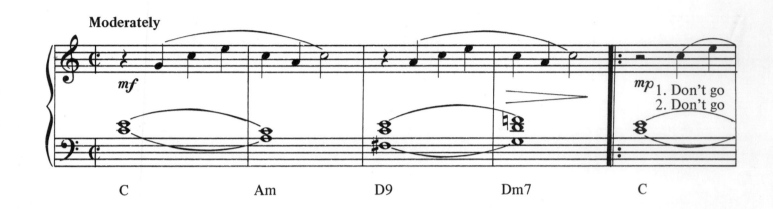

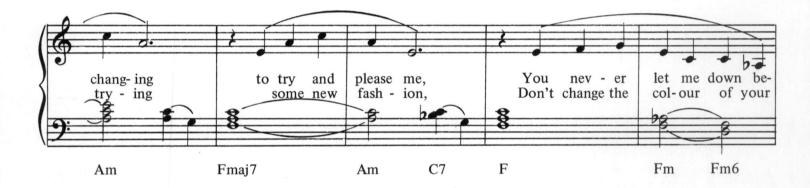

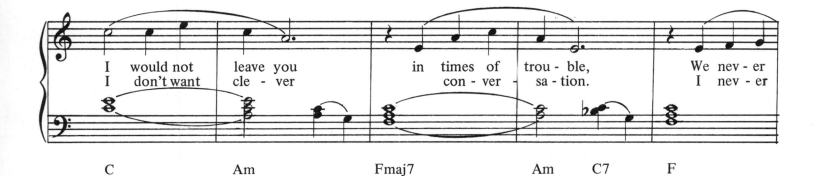

I would not | leave you | in times of | trou - ble, | We nev - er
I don't want | cle - ver | con - ver - | sa - tion. | I nev - er

C   Am   Fmaj7   Am   C7   F

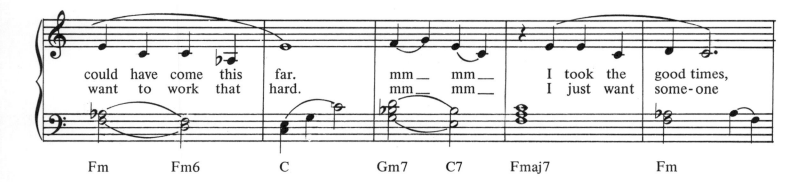

could have come this | far. | mm__ mm__ | I took the | good times,
want to work that | hard. | mm__ mm__ | I just want | some - one

Fm   Fm6   C   Gm7   C7   Fmaj7   Fm

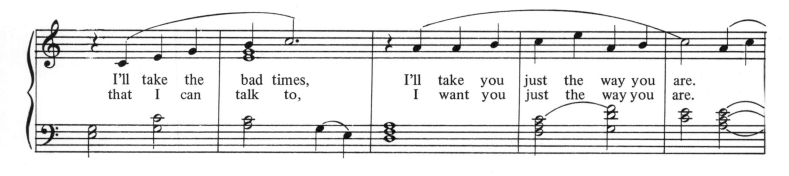

I'll take the | bad times, | I'll take you | just the way you | are.
that I can | talk to, | I want you | just the way you | are.

C   Am   Dm   F   G7   C Am

1   **2**

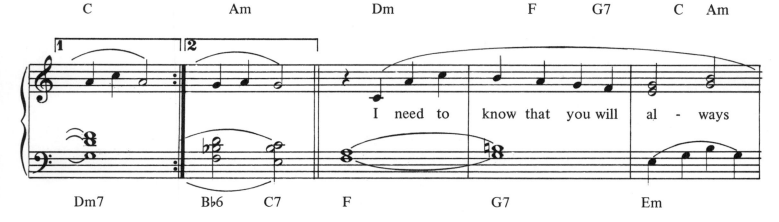

I need to | know that you will | al - ways

Dm7   Bb6   C7   F   G7   Em

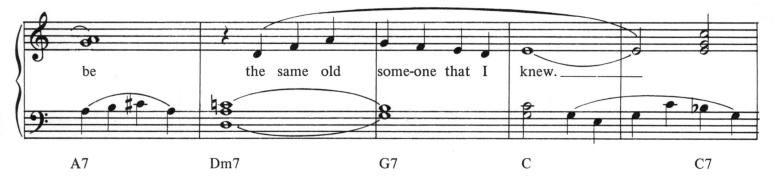

be | the same old | some - one that I | knew.____

A7   Dm7   G7   C   C7

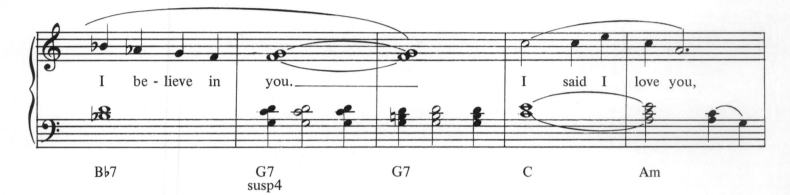

What will it take till you be-lieve in me,   The way that

Ab   Bb7   Gm7   C   Fm

I be - lieve in you. _____   I said I love you,

Bb7   G7   G7   C   Am
         susp4

and that's for - ev - er,   And this I pro - mise from the heart.

F   Am C7   F   Fm Fm6   C

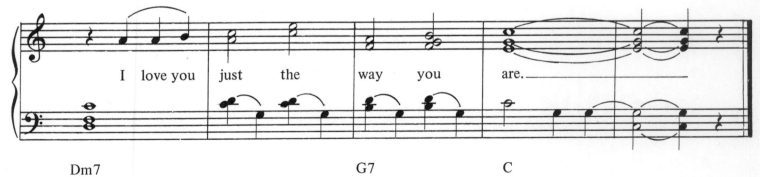

mm___ mm___ I could not love you   an - y___ bet -ter,

Gm7   C7   Fmaj7   Fm   C   Am7

I love you just   the   way   you   are.___

Dm7   G7   C

Take That Look Off Your Face

Words by Don Black
Music by Andrew Lloyd Webber

Steady four

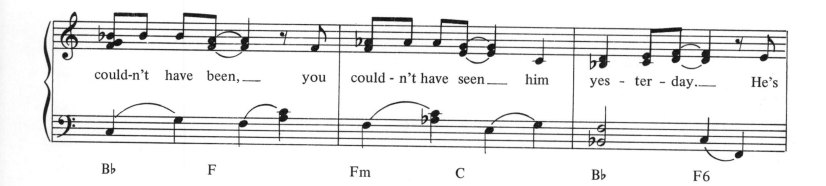

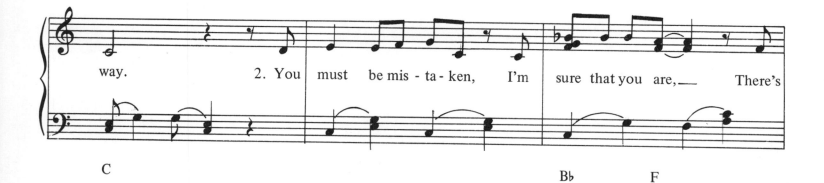

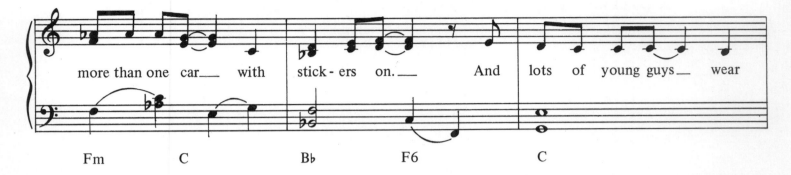

more than one car___ with stick-ers on.___ And lots of young guys___ wear

Fm   C   Bb   F6   C

CHORUS

cor-du-roy pants___ and I'd know___ if he had-n't gone.___ Take that

Am   F   G7   C

look off your face,___ (Take that look off your face___) I can see thru your smile.___ (I can
did-n't dig deep.___ (No I did-n't dig deep___) I did not want to know.___ (I did

C   G7

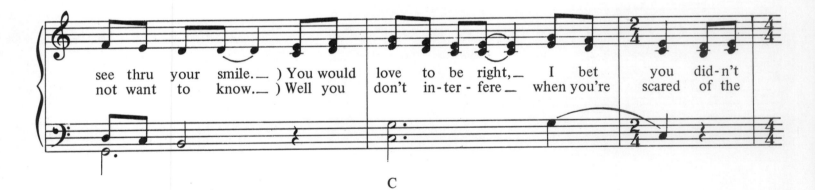

see thru your smile.___) You would love to be right,___ I bet you did-n't
not want to know.___) Well you don't in-ter-fere___ when you're scared of the

                              C

sleep good last night,___ could-n't wait to bring all of that bad___ news to my
things you might hear___ when he's back, you think I will end it___ right there and

G7   F7

To Coda ⊕

door. / then. Well I've got news for you, / Well my fair wea-ther friend, I knew be- / You're wrong a-

Am   F7   F

fore. / gain.   3. If I'm not mis-ta-ken, it start-ed last year.__ I'm

C   (C)   Bb   F

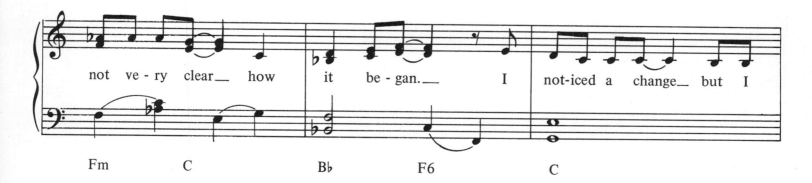

not ve-ry clear__ how it be-gan.__ I not-iced a change__ but I

Fm   C   Bb   F6   C

D.%. al Coda

just closed my eyes__ as on-ly a wo-man__ can. No I

Am   F   G7   C

⊕ CODA

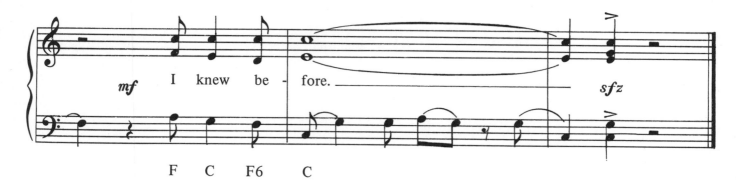

mf   I knew be-fore._____   sfz

F   C   F6   C

19

Bright Eyes

Words and Music by Mike Batt

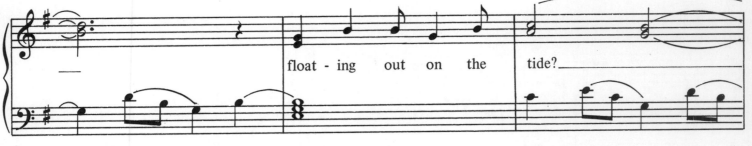

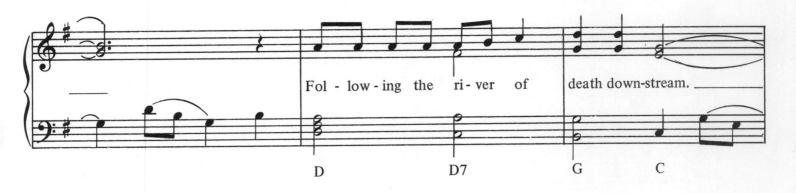

Oh, is it a dream? _____ There's a

C   Am   D7   no chord

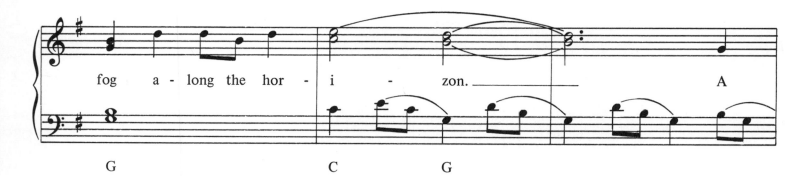

fog a - long the hor - i - zon. _____ A

G   C   G

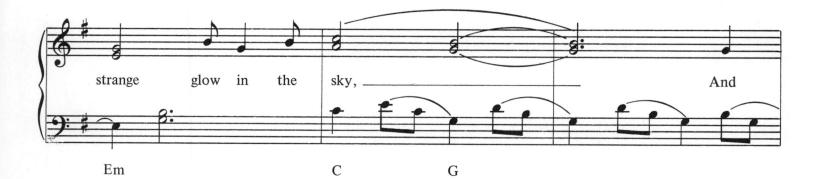

strange   glow   in   the   sky, _____ And

Em   C   G

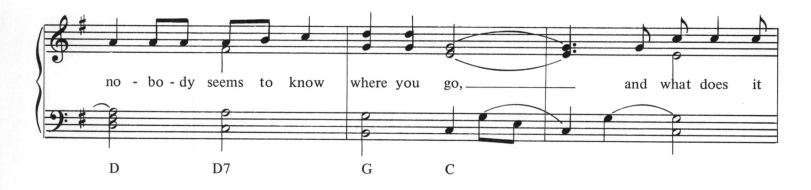

no - bo - dy seems to know   where you   go, _____ and what does it

D   D7   G   C

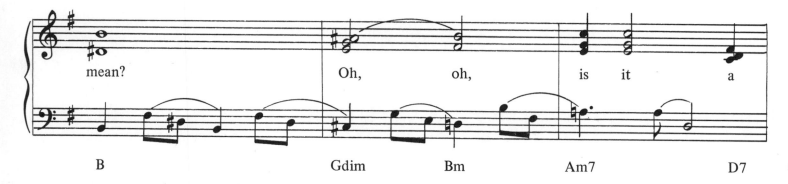

mean?   Oh,   oh,   is   it   a

B   Gdim   Bm   Am7   D7

21

dream? _____ Bright _____ eyes

G   Bm

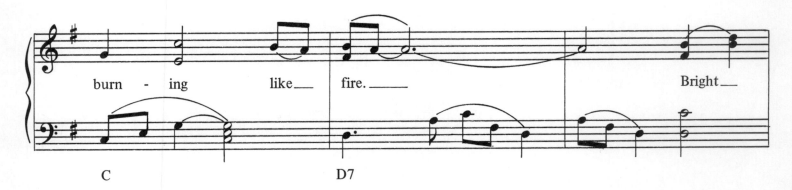

burn - ing   like ___ fire. _____   Bright ___

C   D7

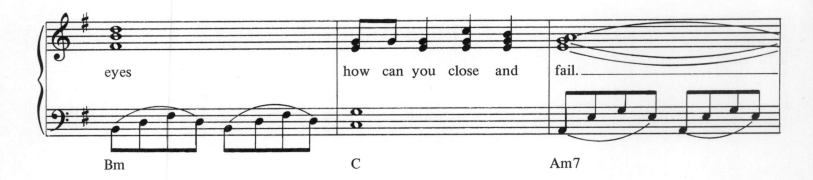

eyes   how can you close and   fail. _____

Bm   C   Am7

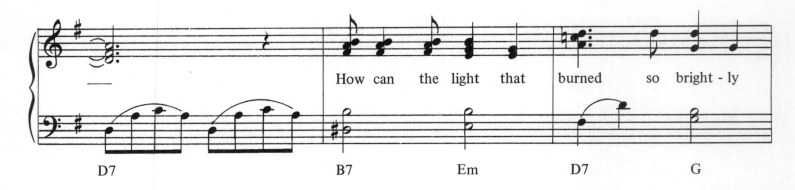

How can   the light that   burned   so   bright - ly

D7   B7   Em   D7   G

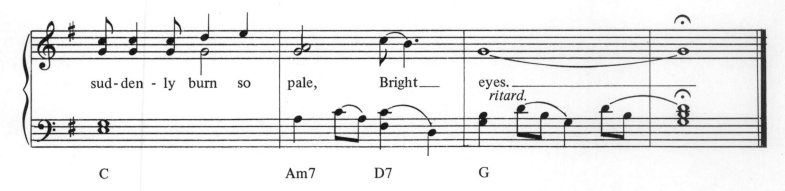

sud - den - ly burn so   pale,   Bright ___   eyes. _____

                                                                    ritard.

C   Am7   D7   G

Wave

Words and Music by Antonio Carlos Jobim

geth-er. _____ You can't de - ny   don't try to fight the ris - ing

Cm7   F   C   F7   C   Fdim

sea.   don't fight the   moon, the   stars a - bove___   and don't fight

Gm7   C7(♭9)   F   Fm6

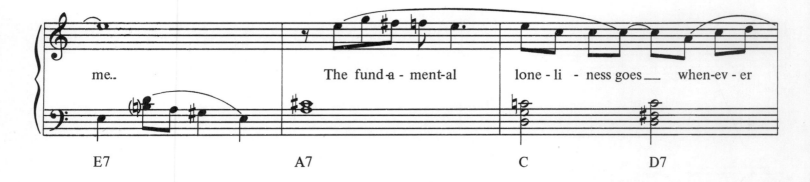

me..   The fund-a - ment-al   lone - li - ness goes___ when-ev - er

E7   A7   C   D7

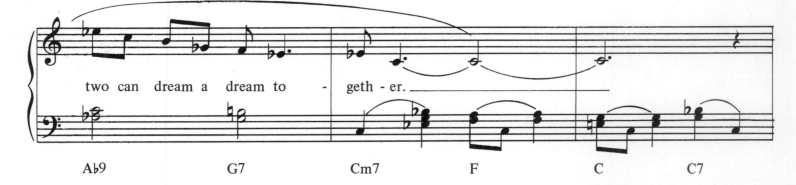

two can dream a   dream to - geth - er. _____

A♭9   G7   Cm7   F   C   C7

When   I saw you   first,   the time was   half   past three.___

Fm7   B♭7   Gm7

24

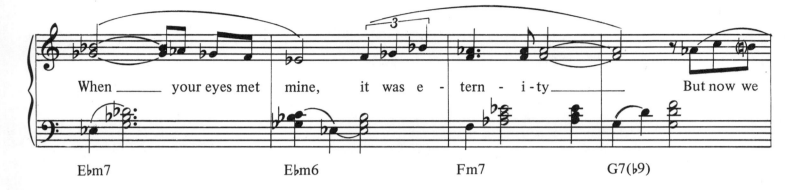

When _____ your eyes met mine, it was e - tern - i - ty _____ But now we

Ebm7   Ebm6   Fm7   G7(b9)

know   the wave is on its way to   be,

C   Fdim   Gm7

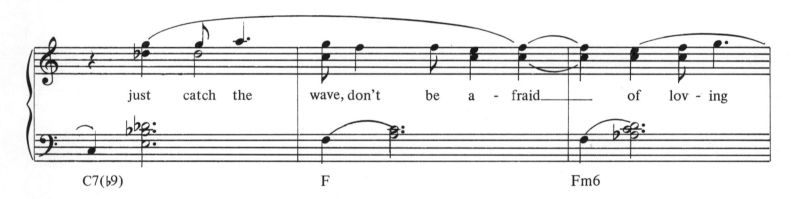

just catch the   wave, don't be a - fraid _____ of lov - ing

C7(b9)   F   Fm6

me.   The fund-a ment - al   lone - li - ness goes ___ whenev-er

E7   A7   C   D7

ritard

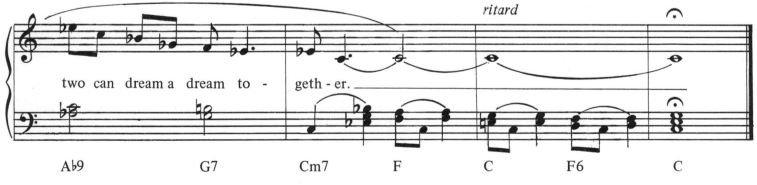

two can dream a dream to - geth - er. _____

Ab9   G7   Cm7   F   C   F6   C

Raindrops Keep Falling On My Head

Words by Hal David
Music by Burt Bacharach

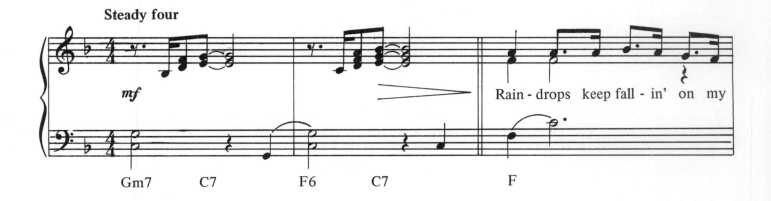

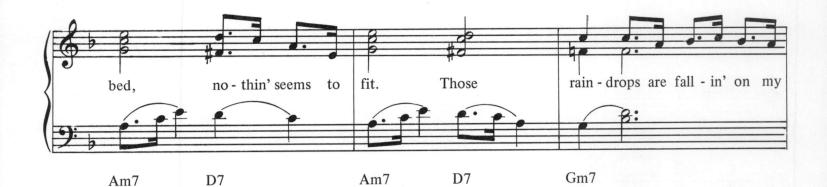

sun. _____ And I said I did-n't like the way he got things

Fmaj7   F7   B♭

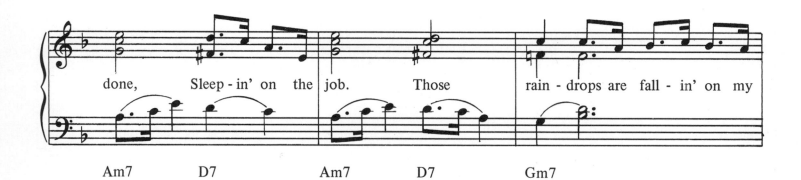

done, Sleep-in' on the job. Those rain-drops are fall-in' on my

Am7   D7   Am7   D7   Gm7

head. They keep fall-in'! But there's one thing I

                                        C7   F

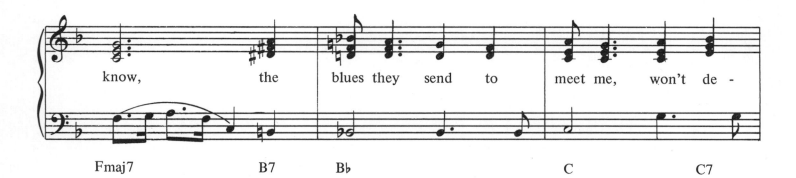

know, the blues they send to meet me, won't de-

Fmaj7   B7   B♭   C   C7

feat me. It won't be long ___ till hap-pi-ness steps

Am7   D7

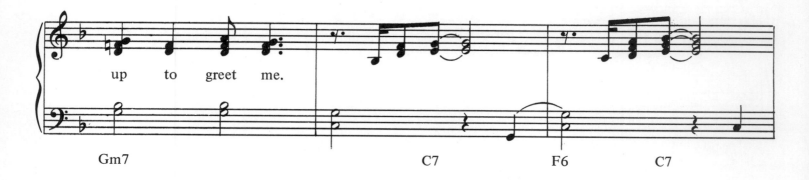

Gm7   C7   F6   C7

up to greet me.

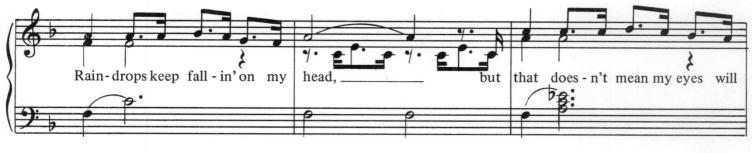

Rain - drops keep fall - in' on my head, _____ but that does - n't mean my eyes will

F   Fmaj7   F7

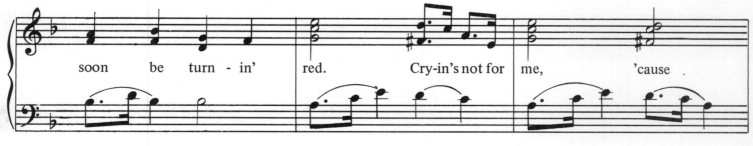

soon be turn - in' red. Cry-in's not for me, 'cause

B♭   Am7   D7   Am7   D7

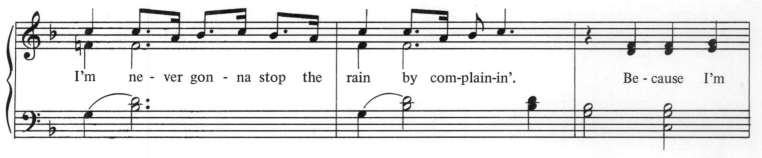

I'm ne - ver gon - na stop the rain by com-plain-in'. Be - cause I'm

Gm7   C7

free,   no - thin's wor-ry - in' me. _____

F   Fmaj7   Gm7   F

Can't Smile Without You

Words and Music by Chris Arnold, David Martin and Geoff Morrow

Am   Am7

you___ on-ly knew what I'm___ go-ing through;   I just can't   smile___ with-out

Em   Am7   Gmaj7   Am7   G   Em7

you.   You came a - long   just like a song and

Am7   C   D7   G   Em7

bright-ened my day. Who'd a be-lieved that you were part of a dream?   Now it all seems

Am7   D   C   D7   Am7

light years a - way.   And now you know I   smile,   Now

Dm7   G7   C

some peo-ple say   hap - pi-ness takes   so ve-ry long to find.___ Well, I'm

finding it hard, leav-ing your love be-hind me. And you see, I

Cm   Am7   D7

can't smile with-out you, I can't smile with-out you. I

G   Em7

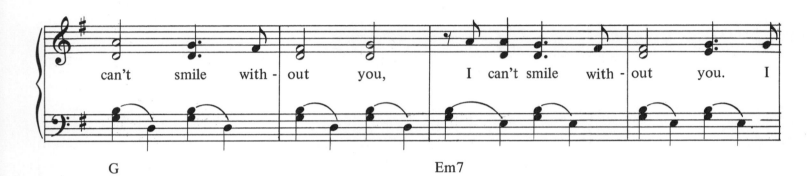

can't laugh and I can't sing. I'm find-ing it hard to do an-y-thing. You see, I

Am   Am7   D7

feel glad when you're glad. I feel sad when you're sad. If
you.

G   Em

Repeat and Fade

you_ on-ly knew what I'm_ go-ing through; I just can't smile with-out

Am   Am7

You Light Up My Life

Words and Music by Joe Brooks

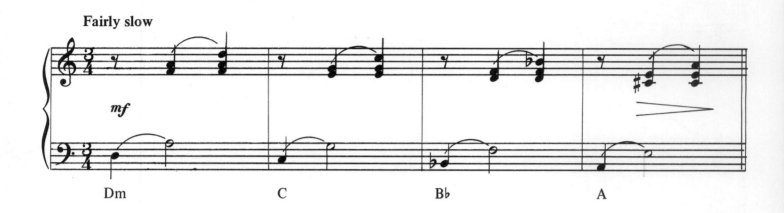

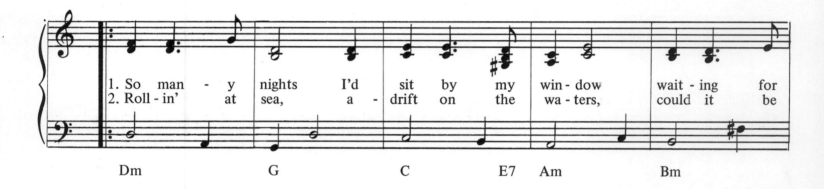

1. So man - y nights I'd sit by my win - dow, wait - ing for
2. Roll - in' at sea, a - drift on the wa - ters, could it be

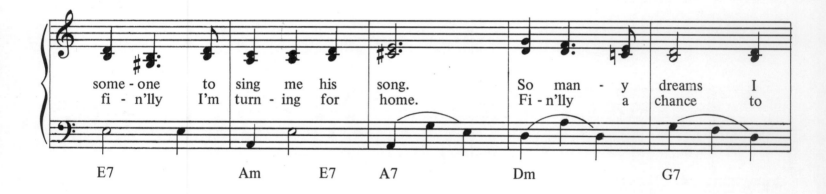

some - one to sing me his song. So man - y dreams I
fi - n'lly I'm turn - ing for home. Fi - n'lly a chance to

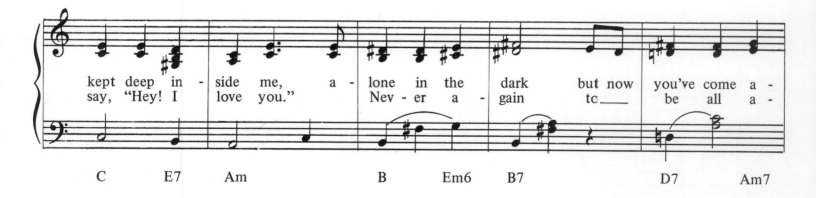

kept deep in - side me, a - lone in the dark but now you've come a -
say, "Hey! I love you." Nev - er a - gain to___ be all a -

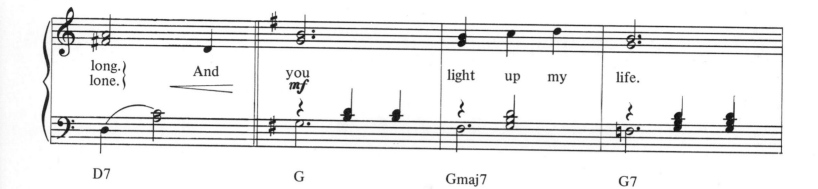

long. / lone. } And you light up my life.

D7   G   Gmaj7   G7

You give me hope, to car - ry on. You light up my

G F#7b5 Dm E7   Am6 E Am   Am7 G C

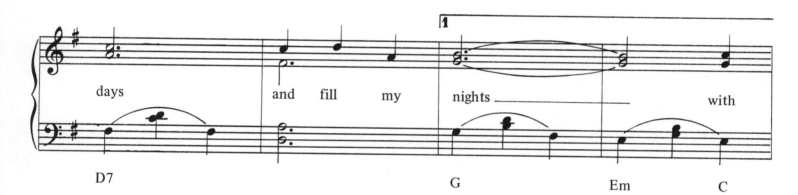

1.

days and fill my nights _____ with

D7   G   Em   C

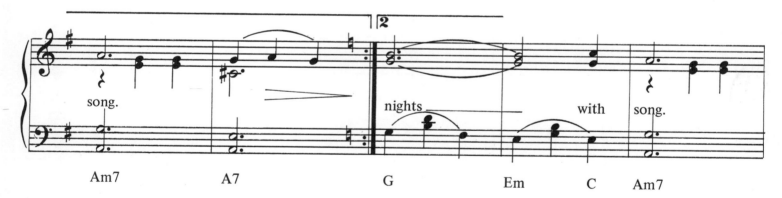

2.

song. nights _____ with song.

Am7   A7   G   Em   C   Am7

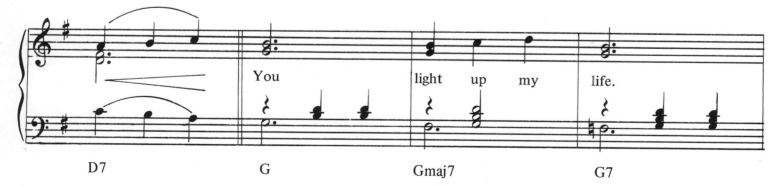

You light up my life.

D7   G   Gmaj7   G7

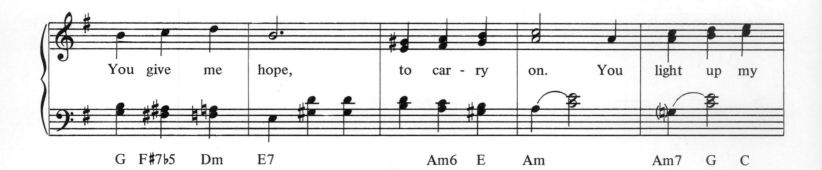

You give me hope, to car-ry on. You light up my

G F#7b5 Dm E7 Am6 E Am Am7 G C

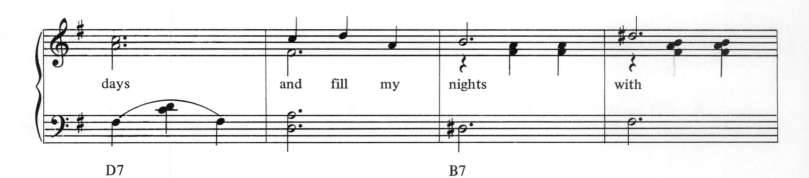

days and fill my nights with

D7 B7

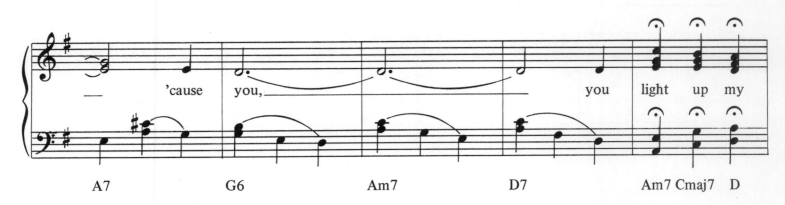

song. It can't be wrong when it feels so right,____

Em7 A7 G B7 Em7

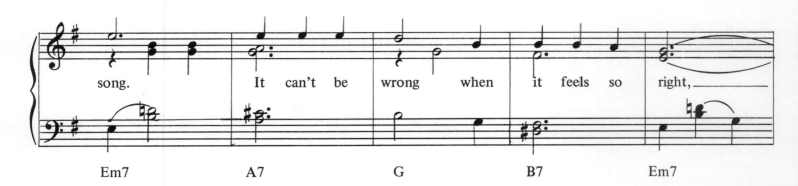

__ 'cause you,____ you light up my

A7 G6 Am7 D7 Am7 Cmaj7 D

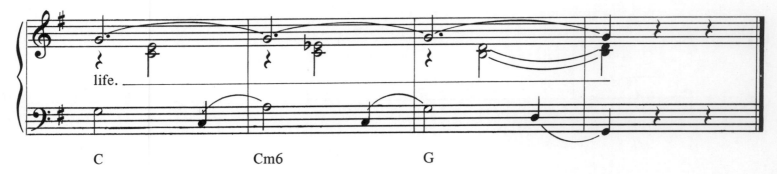

life.____

C Cm6 G

Sailing

Words and Music by Gavin Sutherland

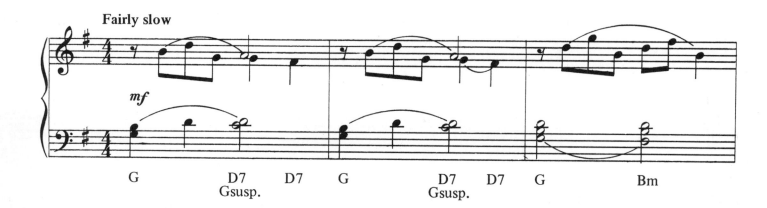

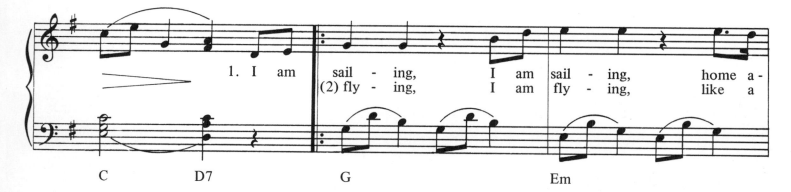

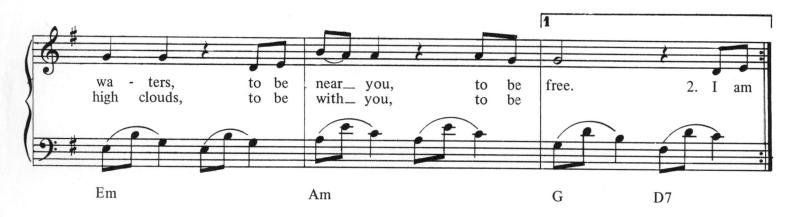

free.   Can you   hear me,   can you   hear me,   through the

G   D7   G   Em

dark night   far   a - way.   I am   dy - ing, ____ for - ev - er

C   G   A7

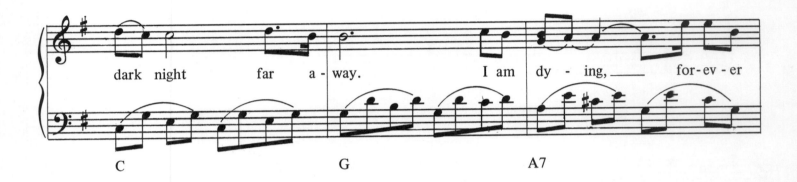

try - ing   to be   with __ you   who can   say.   Can you

Em   A   G   Am7   D7

hear me,   can you   hear me,   Thro' the   dark night   far a -

G   Em   C

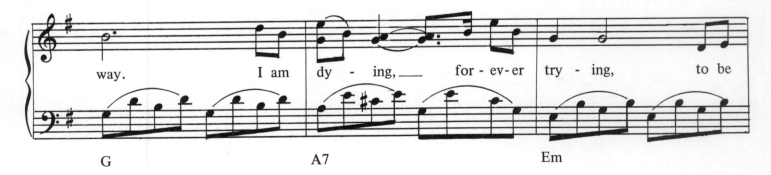

way.   I am   dy - ing, ____ for - ev - er   try - ing,   to be

G   A7   Em

with__ you who can say.   We are

Am   G   D7

sail - ing, we are sail - ing, Home a - gain __ 'cross the

G   Em   C

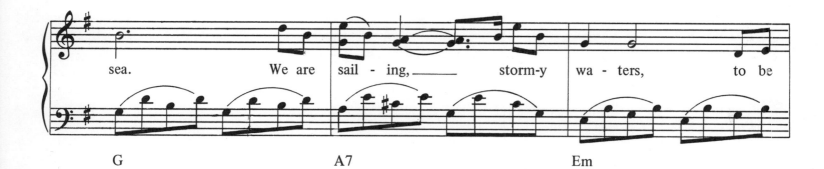

sea.   We are sail - ing, _____ storm-y wa - ters, to be

G   A7   Em

near__ you to be free. Oh Lord to be near__ you, to be

Am   G   D7 Am

Repeat and fade

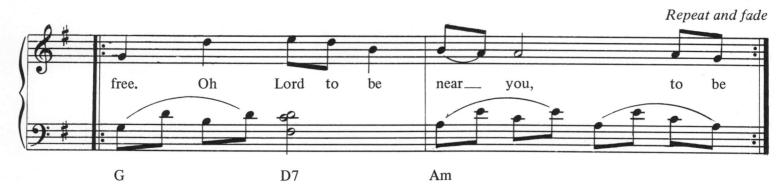

free. Oh Lord to be near__ you,   to be

G   D7   Am

You Don't Bring Me Flowers

Words by Neil Diamond, Marilyn Bergman and Alan Bergman
Music by Neil Diamond

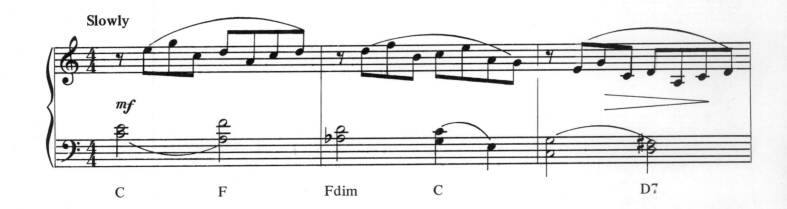

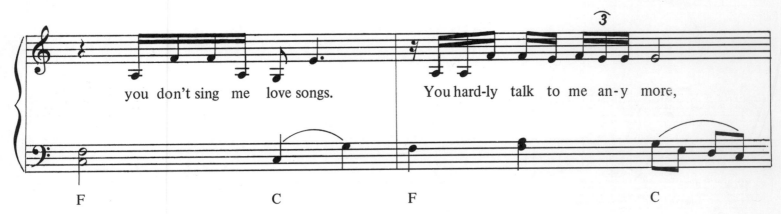

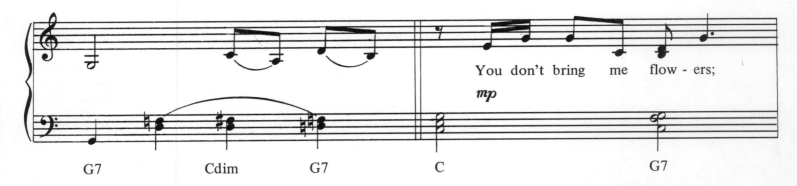

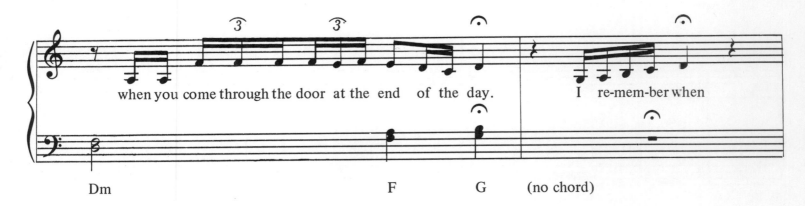

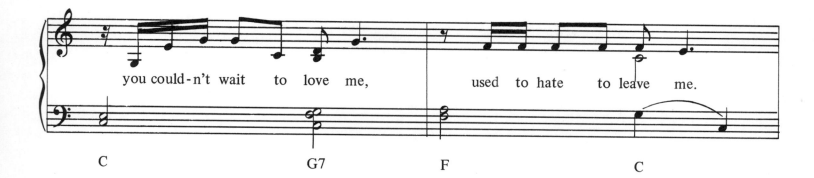

you could-n't wait to love me, used to hate to leave me.

C   G7   F   C

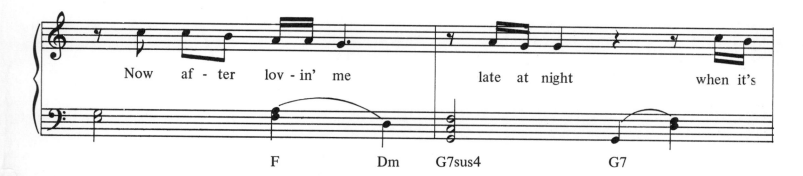

Now af - ter lov - in' me late at night when it's

F   Dm   G7sus4   G7

good for you and you're feel - in' all right, well, you

C   F   C   G7

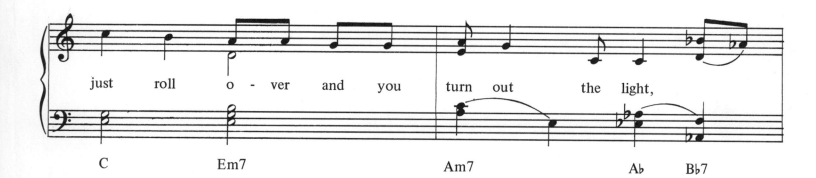

just roll o - ver and you turn out the light,

C   Em7   Am7   A♭   B♭7

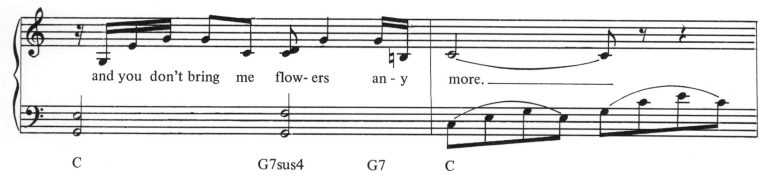

and you don't bring me flow - ers an - y more.

C   G7sus4   G7   C

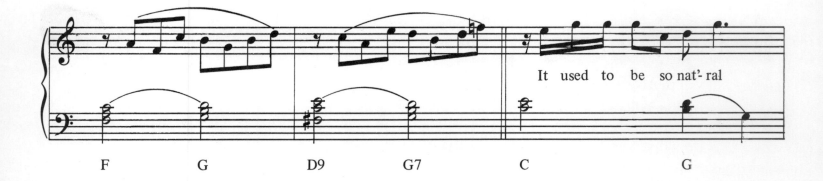

F   G   D9   G7   C   G

It used to be so nat'-ral

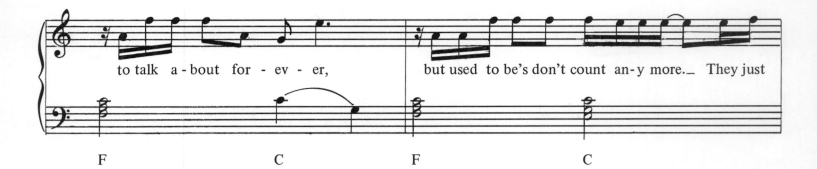

F   C   F   C

to talk a-bout for - ev - er,   but used to be's don't count an-y more.___ They just

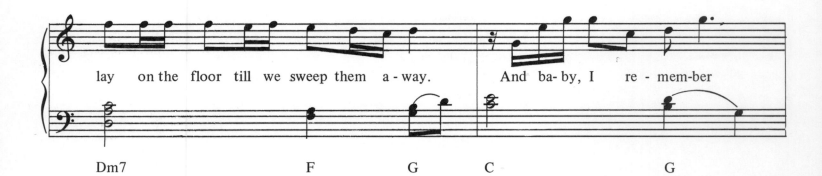

Dm7   F   G   C   G

lay   on the floor till we sweep them a - way.   And ba- by, I   re - mem-ber

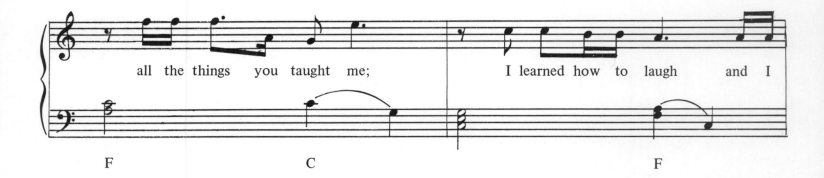

F   C   F

all the things   you taught me;   I learned how to laugh   and I

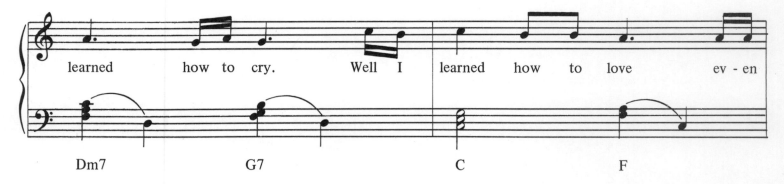

Dm7   G7   C   F

learned   how to cry.   Well I   learned how to love   ev - en

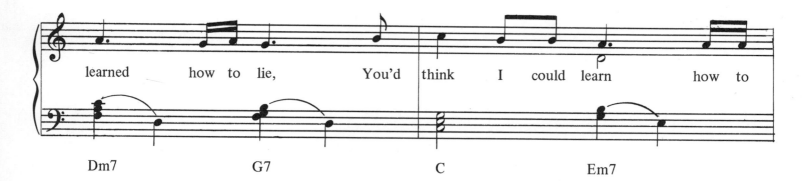

learned how to lie, You'd think I could learn how to

Dm7   G7   C   Em7

tell you good-bye, _____ 'cause you don't bring me flow-ers an-y

Am   Ab Bb7   C   G7sus4   G7

more. _____ Well, you'd think I could learn how to

Am7   C6   F   G   C   Em7

tell you good-bye, _____ 'cause you don't bring me flow-ers an-y

Am7   Ab Bb7   C   G7sus4   G7

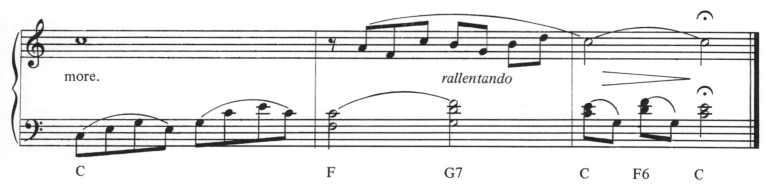

more.   *rallentando*

C   F   G7   C F6 C

I Write The Songs

Words and Music by Bruce Johnston

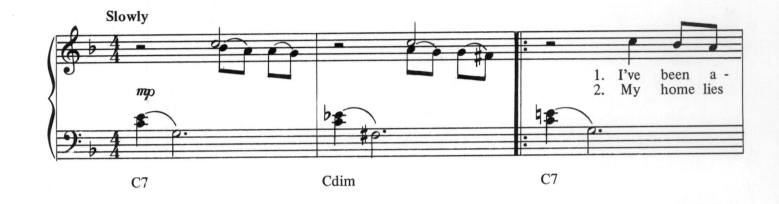

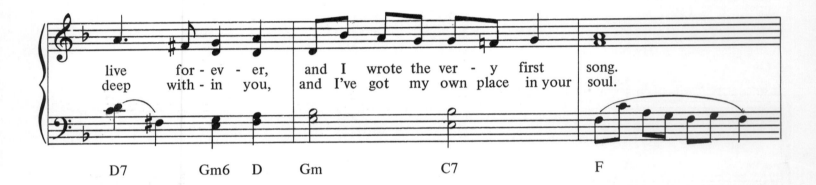

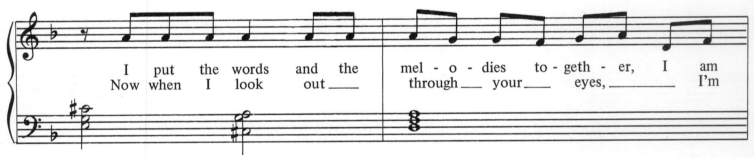

I write the songs that make the whole world sing, I write the songs of love and

F   Gm   C7

spe - cial things.   I write the songs that make the young girls cry.

F   Dm   G7

I write the songs, I write the songs.   songs.   Oh my

Gm7   F   F

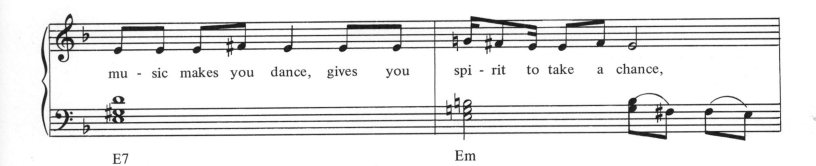

mu - sic makes you dance, gives you   spi - rit to take a chance,

E7   Em

And I wrote some rock 'n roll so   you'd feel so good,   My

A

43

G7   C7   G

mu - sic fills your heart, well, that's a real fine place to start, it's from

Gm7   C7

me, it's for you, it's from you, it's for me, it's a world wide sym - pho - ny.___

F   Gm   C7

I write the songs that make the whole world sing, I write the songs of love and

F   Dm

spe - cial things. I write the songs that make the

G7   Gm7   F

young girls cry. I write the songs, I write the songs.___

ritard.

One Day At A Time

Words and Music by Marijohn Wilkin and Kris Kristofferson

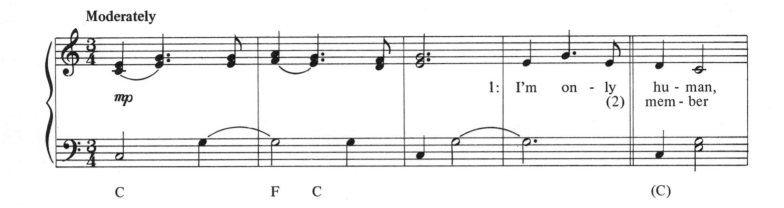

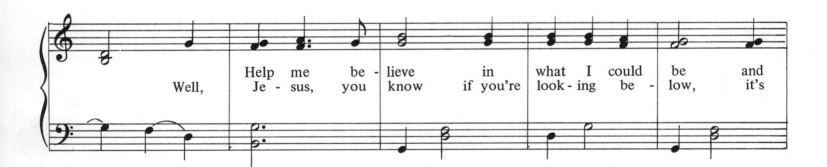

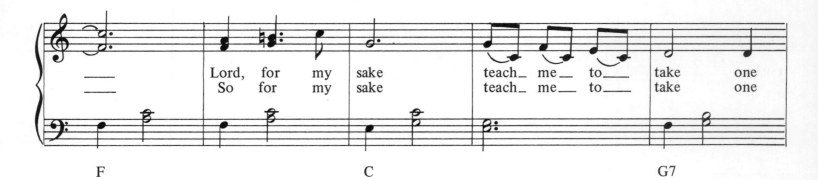

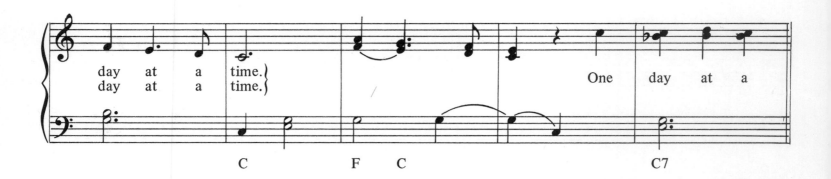

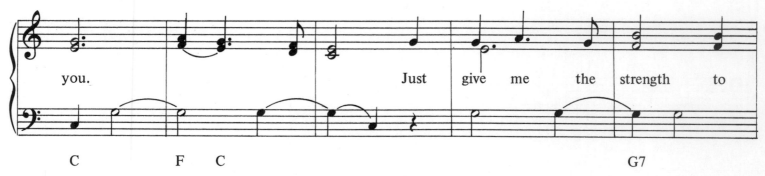

46

do ev - 'ry day what I have to do.

C

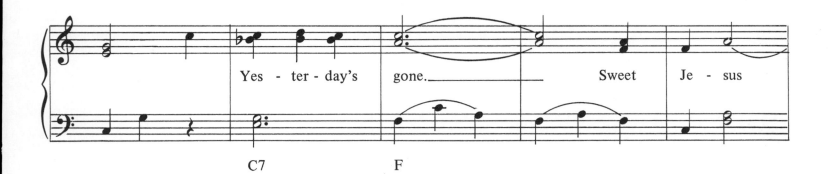

Yes - ter - day's gone._____ Sweet Je - sus

C7   F

and to - mor - row may nev - er be mine.

Dm   C   F   C

Lord, help me to - day, show me the way one

G7

day at a time.   2. Do you re -

C   F   C

10/90 (10677)